RAZZLE DAZZLE

Also published by Hands Up Books

A Bag of Stars (Poems for Children) Collected by Graham Denton

Giving You the 'Willies'! (Delightfully Devilish Verse…and much, much worse!) Collected by Graham Denton

Dancing with Frankenstein and Other Limericks by Robert Scotellaro

Snail Stampede and Other Poems by Robert Scotellaro

Spider-flavoured Sausages by Daphne Kitching

Wanted Alive by Bernard Young

On My Way to School I Saw a Dinosaur by Roger Stevens

A Stegosaurus is for Life and Other Animal Poems by Trevor Millum

Mrs. Pringle's Jolly Jingles by Linda Knaus

Hey, Little Bug! by James Carter

Shouting at the Ocean: Poems that make a splash! Edited by Graham Denton, Andrea Shavick and Roger Stevens

A Bug in My Hair! and Other Poems by Ian Bland and Philip Waddell

RAZZLE DAZZLE

POEMS BY
ANDY SEED

ILLUSTRATIONS BY
KATE DAUBNEY

HANDS UP BOOKS

To Finley.

With special thanks to Graham Denton.

ISBN 978-0-9555589-2-4

First published 2010 by Hands Up Books
www.handsupbooks.co.uk

For further information, please contact:
Graham Denton (editor),
1 New Cottages, Spout Hill,
Brantingham, East Riding of Yorkshire
HU15 1QW

Printed in the UK by York Publishing Services

CONTENTS

Razzle Dazzle

Razzle-dazzle
Tip-top
Mish-mash
Flip-flop

Chit-chat
Sing-song
Hurly-burly
Ding-dong

Tittle-tattle
Nick-nack
Ping-pong
Tick-tack

Helter-skelter
Namby-pampy
Hoity-toity
Hanky-panky

Pell-mell
Slip-slop
See-saw
Stip-stop!

The Purple Pigs of Pluto

The purple pigs of Pluto
Are as large as jumbo jets;
They eat rocks and dust and satellites
And keep astronauts as pets.

The purple pigs of Pluto
Go dancing out at noon;
They wear suits and boots and parachutes
And yodel out of tune.

The purple pigs of Pluto
Reside in gloomy craters;
Where they dream of stars and choccy bars
Served up with mashed potaters.

The purple pigs of Pluto
Have but one desire from birth:
To travel a lot, and – guess what –
They're thinking of coming to *Earth*!

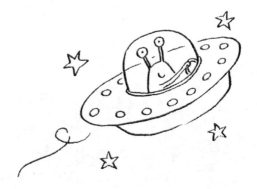

Mum, I Saw an Alien

Mum, I saw an alien,
It's out there on the road!
With orange hair and bloodshot eyes,
And skin as warty as a toad.

It's coming closer, mum – watch out,
Those yellow teeth look mean;
That great big belly scares me,
And its clothes are strange and green.

It's making funny noises,
And walking like a grouse;
With drooling lips and crooked nose –
It's coming towards our house!

Let's see this alien then, said mum,
With the courage of a lion,
Out there you say? Don't be daft –
That's just your Uncle Brian.

Cheese and Crackers

Some people
Think
The Moon
Is made of
Cheese.

They must
Be
Crackers.

Chocolate in the House

There's chocolate in the house,
I hear it calling me.
There's chocolate in the house,
I can't stay away.
There's chocolate in the house,
It's drawing me near.
There's chocolate in the house,
To resist is useless.
There's chocolate in the house,
I'll just go and see what kind it is.
There's chocolate in the house,
It's a good kind.
There's chocolate in the house,
I'll just try a bit.
There's chocolate in the house,
Mmmmm…
There's chocolate in the house,
Smooth and creamy…
There's no chocolate in the house.

Love at First Bite

It all started so well.
I met him in a bar;
He was dark and handsome,
Smooth and rich, too.
I suggested going for a bite;
I held him in my arms,
Our lips touched;
I melted his heart.

That was last week.
He's gone now;
It all went to pieces
(He was a bit of a square).

That's the trouble
When you fall in love
With chocolate.

Best Eat Lean

Jack Spratt
Could eat no fat,
His wife could eat no lean;
Now she can only
Get through doors
With the aid of margarine.

King Kong's Car Boot Sale

1 biplane (slightly damaged),
1 TV aerial from Empire State Building (needs attention),
6 photos of New York,
12,000 banana skins,
4 copies of *Oversized Ape Monthly* (mint condition),
1 pair underpants (XXXXXXXL).

A Picture's Worth a Thousand Words

A picture's worth
A thousand words
They say,
But when I handed in
Two photos of my cat
And a postcard of Bridlington
Instead of a
3000 word essay
At school,
I got done.

Don't always believe
What they say.

My Grandad

My grandad
Was hurt in the war.
He has a wooden leg
And a glass eye.
Mum says he has plastic teeth too;
Dad says he has nerves of steel.
Grandad also told me he has a rubber bum.
He says it's more comfortable for sitting on.
I don't believe it.
Plastic teeth?

Sort Yourself Out

Pull a face,
Poke an eye,
Bend an ear,
Heave a sigh.

Scratch your head,
Wiggle your toes,
Wash your hands,
Blow your nose.

Pick a scab,
Squeeze a spot,
Crick your neck,
Scratch your bot.

Crack your knuckles,
Furrow your brow,
Cut your toenails,
Sorted now?

Upgrading Granny

Granny's been to the hospital,
She needed an upgrade again;
Her body's been stripped and refitted,
By an army of white-coated men.

Her new teeth are pure carbon fibre,
Her specs were designed with a laser;
She can now bite through plates if she wants to,
And her eyesight's as sharp as a razor.

She's got digital hearing aid power,
And her pacemaker's nuclear I'm told;
They replaced her hip with a stainless steel joint,
And her Zimmer's now radio controlled.

There was a special offer on memory,
She got 64 megs of it free;
She can now recall where she left grandad,
And that that I owe her 35p.

Her toilet's controlled by computer,
Her electric shopping cart's fun;
Her stairlift's got internet access,
I can't wait till I'm ninety one.

The Dreaded Mrs Hyde

Help! here comes that dinner lady,
The dreaded Mrs Hyde;
She's six foot seven inches tall
And surely just as wide.

She cannot talk, she always shouts
And makes the infants sob;
The juniors just pull faces
And say, 'Shhh – here's the blob!'

Her stare can turn the custard cold,
Her eyes are sharp as thistles;
And when they're serving lumpy stew
She makes you eat the gristle.

She always cries for 'silence!'
But silence won't come near,
For she makes more noise just by herself
Than all the children here.

And when it reaches playtime,
The children rush outside
Followed by the sound of doom –
The dreaded Mrs Hyde...

Queue for the Nurse

Adrian Pitt
Had scores of nits.

Jennifer Crumb
Had a bleeding thumb.

Stanley Butts
Had griping guts.

Melanie Black
Had an itchy back.

Vernon Firms
Had 'orrible worms.

Rita Spry
Had a fly in her eye.

Reuben Groat
Had a lump in his throat,

And Sally Futtock
Had a boil on her nose.

There's a Hole in My Sock

There's a hole in my sock,
There's a rip in my shirt,
There's a bum in my pants,
And two legs in my skirt.

There's nits in my hair,
And a stain on my tie,
A boil on my nose,
And a twinkle in my eye.

There's blood in my veins,
And fillings in my teeth,
But there's nothing in my head,
(That's a relief).

Nothing Serious

I thought
I'd broken
My funny bone,
But it was
Nothing serious.

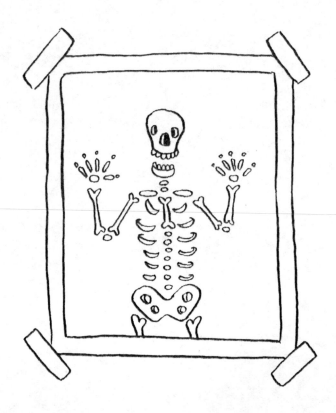

Poorly Class

Barry Smith has caught the flu,
Emily's knees are skinned;
Nicky Spratt ate too much stew,
And Ronny Pigg's got wind.

Sam O'Rourke is plagued with spots,
Peter Wright's been chinned;
Sally has verrucas – lots,
But Ronny Pigg's got wind.

Terry's cough came from his dad,
The teacher's hair has thinned;
But none of this is quite as bad
As Ronny Piggs's wind.

And why with so much illness here
Has everybody grinned?
That's right, just as the teacher feared,
Ronny Pigg's got wind.

Victim of Nature

I've been stung by a scorpion,
I've been bitten by a dog;
Hugged by a bear,
And jumped on by a frog.

I've been spat at by a camel,
Scratched by a cat;
Mauled by a lion,
Had my blood sucked by a bat.

I've been laughed at by hyenas,
Nibbled by a mouse;
Nipped by a naughty crab,
And infested by a louse.

I've been squeezed by a python,
And charged at by a bull;
Teased by a cockatoo,
Pooed on by a gull.

I've been spiked by a hedgehog,
Had ants in my panties;
Kicked by a grumpy horse,
And been preyed on by a mantis.

I've been squirted by a stinky skunk,
And attacked by countless pets;
I've only got myself to blame,
Oh why am I a vet?

Be Careful Patting Ogres

Who's a nice little ogre?
Who's a lovely cuddly ogre?
Who's a big soft chubby ogre?
Who's a gentle jolly ogrery-wogrery then?
OWW!
Can I have my hand back?

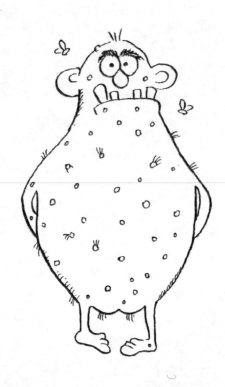

How About it, Santa?

Dear Santa,

For Christmas this year
I'd like:
Peace on Earth,
An end to all violence,
Enough food for the starving millions,
1000 new hospitals,
Love between all races,
And an iPod.

P.S.
Don't worry if you can't manage
All the peace and love stuff.

Bogeyman's Dilemma

She loves me,
She loves me snot;
She loves me,
She loves me snot…

Looby

I was really sad when Looby died,
My favourite pet of all;
We buried her at the back of the house,
Next to the garden wall.

I was really sad when Looby died,
That giraffe was part of my soul;
But not as sad as dad was:
Took him two years to dig the hole.

House of Ill Repute

My computer has a virus,
My fridge has caught a cold;
The cooker has a temperature,
And my antiques are getting old.

The TV is off colour,
My office desk has piles;
The carpet's been run over,
And the bathroom's on the tiles.

The extractor fan has awful wind,
My iron's feeling flat,
The toilet paper's indisposed;
And there's pimples on my ping-pong bat.

Upstairs my pillow's bed-ridden,
Downstairs the chimney's got flue;
Even my best wine is on the rack,
What am I going to do?

Outside, the garden's looking quite green,
And the field next door has been grazed;
The septic tank's turned serious,
Even the daisies look dazed.

Are all these conditions contagious?
Will the whole street follow suit?
Is there a doctor in the house?
My house of ill repute.

Lost Property

I looked in the lost property box.
There were:
Three plimsolls,
A pair of faded red shorts,
Four socks (none matching),
A broken ruler,
Two school jumpers (one torn),
And,
Hang on,
A 1950s bungalow with two bedrooms and a privet hedge.
No –
Put it back,
Mine has three bedrooms.

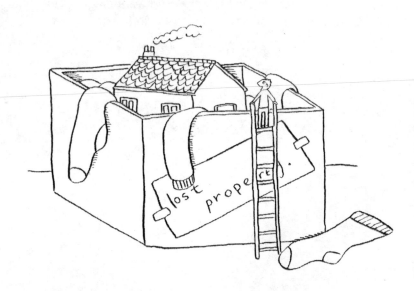

Easy Mistake to Make

Andy Seed

Oh, sorry.
You meant write your
Name and address

The Foul Seasons

(A short poem dedicated to our glorious British weather)

Spring;
> damp and very cold.

Summer;
> damp and cold.

Autumn;
> very damp and cold.

Winter;
> very damp and very cold.

Action Replay

Wembley 1966
       Grasmere Road, Cheadle, 1967
England v Mexico
       Me v a lamppost
Charlton picks up the ball
       Andy Seed picks up a tin can
He surges through midfield
       He surges across the pavement
A trademark body swerve loses the defender
       A brilliant shimmy by-passes the lamppost
He draws back his mighty right foot
       He lines up the tin can with precision
And smashes the ball into the net
       And smashes next door's hall window
Charlton runs away to celebrate
       Seed runs away to hide

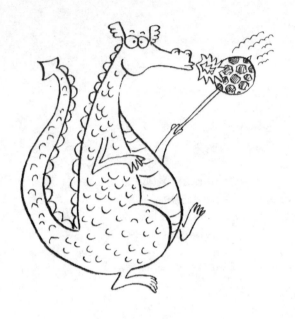

Fancy a Game?

Here's my Monster footie team:

Keeper:
King Kong – he's useless, but he does block the whole goal.

Defenders:
Cyclops – always keeps his eye on the ball;
Pegasus – plays centaur half;
Werewolf – excellent at long loud offside calls;
Phoenix – good in the air (recently made a great comeback too).

Midfield:
Godzilla – provides a bit of bite in the tackle;
Big Foot – free kick specialist;
Dragon – very pacy (burns around the pitch);
Roc – good on the wing.

Attack:
Cerberus – has two sweet left feet;
Medusa – defenders are petrified when she's on form.

Fancy a game?

The Rev Spooner's Shopping List

Jaspberry ram
Chot hocolate
Ninger guts
Beggie vurger
Sea poup
Spixed mice
Lairy fiquid
Bea tags
Pushroom mizza
Chini meddars
Jackcurrant belly
Poo laper
Nicken choodles
Haghetti spoops
Lire fighters
Glubber roves
Sup a coup
Poothtaste
Palf a hound of Chensleydale wheese
and
Baked beans
(Gank thoodness)

Household Chores

I answered the door
(it asked me what the time was),

And took out the rubbish
(to see a James Bond film),

And put on the washing machine
(although it didn't fit very well),

Then drew the curtains
(until my pencil lead snapped),

And cleared my desk
(with a mighty leap),

And finally, fed the goldfish
(to the cat).

Fairy Tale Questions

Who were The Three Bears forebears?
Why did Little Miss Muffet?
Was Red Riding Hood hurt when the woodcutt'er?
Did you see Puss in Boots when you were shopping?
Why is Rapunzel so uptight? She should let her hair down once in a while.
Does this year's panto have Aladdin?
Why couldn't Jack keep a secret? Beanstalk, I suppose.
Is Pinocchio lying again? Who nose!

First Drafts

The Owl and the Pussy Cat went to ~~Wigan~~ ~~mow~~ ~~KFC~~ sea

Double, double, toil and ~~upset~~ ~~bad news~~ ~~difficulty~~ trouble

Tyger! Tyger! burning ~~coal~~ ~~bridges~~ ~~down the motorway~~ bright

This is the night mail crossing the ~~road~~ ~~t's~~ ~~line~~ border

I met a traveller from an antique ~~shop~~ ~~desk~~ ~~dealer~~ land

I wandered lonely as a ~~lonely person~~ ~~gate~~ ~~furniture van~~ cloud

You Can't Go Wrong with the Classics

A bookless kid,
I once asked granny
What to read.

'Oh you can't go wrong
With the classics,'
She said.

'Like What?'

'You know –
AA Barrie,
JM Graham,
Kenneth Milne,
All of those.'

'Never heard of them.'

'What!
You must know
Winnie the Willows,
The Wind in the Pan
And Peter Poo.'

'Hang on,
That's not right.
It's Winnie the Pan,
Peter with the Wind
And Pan the Poo.'

'Or is it
Poo in the Willows,
Winnie the Wind
And Pan Peter?

'Anyway,
They're classics.'

Made Up

When the Romans conquered Europe,
They made a great empire.

When Marie Curie discovered radium,
She made a great scientific breakthrough.

When Hitler invaded Russia,
He made a grave mistake.

When Neil Armstrong stepped onto the moon,
He made history.

When Auntie Marjorie and Uncle Kevin came to tea,
I made eggy toast.

All Roads

They say that all roads
Lead to Rome,
And all footpaths
Lead to Frinton;
All railways
Go to Ross-on-Wye,
And all lanes
Just stop at Linton.

Or do all roads really
Roam to Leeds?
And all pavements
Plod to Poole?
Does every alley
End at Ayr?
And each bridleway
At Goole?

No, I lied about
The footpaths,
And the rest
Is all untrue;
And who said
All roads
Lead to Rome?
Cos that is rubbish too.

Travels with My Ankle

Sometimes
I get my
Mords wuddled up,
And I'm clumsy,
Like
When I hent on woliday
To the seaside
With my ankle,
And broke my uncle.

School Trip Quotes

(A poem for a class having a day out at the seaside)

'Are we nearly there yet?' said Miles.
'Aw, it's taking ages,' said Mona.
'I don't feel well,' said Chuck.
'Oh, you'll be fine,' said Faith.
'Let's have a sing-song,' said Carol.
'The sun's out at last,' said Ray.
'What a wonderful day,' said Joy.
'Let's go to the beach,' said Sandy.
'Yeah - and build sandcastles,' said Doug.
'I want to fish in rock pools,' said Annette.
'Don't go near the edge,' said Cliff.
'And mind the stones,' said Rocky.
'Are there any wild animals round here?' said Claude.
'I need a drink,' said Phil.
'Make mine a big one,' said Max.
'How much do they cost?' said Bill.
'This one was free,' said Nick.
'Can we go now? I need a wee,' said Lou.

Queue

I've stood in this queue
To go to the lueue
Since quarter past tueue
It's perfectly trueue
– Oh what shall I dueue?

The Boys in My Class

The boys
In my class
Can't keep
Still:

Bob'll bobble
Jack'll cackle
Rob'll wobble
Tom'll tackle
Tod'll toddle
Sid'll fiddle
Wilf'll waddle
Tim'll twiddle
Mat'll battle
Nick'll tickle
Pat'll rattle
Pete'll prickle
Rab'll babble
Stig'll wiggle
Guy'll gabble
And Jef'll jiggle.

See.

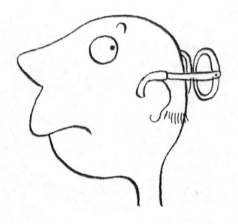

Hindsight

Yesterday
I went to get my hindsight tested.
It was perfect.
Looking back,
I should have known that.

I'm Telling

You looked at me –
I'm telling.
You touched my book –
I'm telling.
You're chewing gum –
I'm telling.
Ouch! That hurt –
I'm telling.
You've pinched my trousers!
I'm telling.
You've eaten my pencil case!
I'm telling.
You've set the classroom on fire!
I'm telling.
You've invaded Poland!
I'm telling.

You don't take much notice do you?

I'm telling.

Limericks

There once was a boy from Nevada,
Whose teacher said, 'You must try hada,
To spell words in History,
It isn't a mystery –
We'll start with the Spanish Armader.'

In a tall dark building in Florida,
There's a long and miserable corridor,
The rooms are no fun,
Esp 101,
Its contents could hardly be horrider.

There was a young lady of Frome,
Who rented *The Temple of Dome*,
Expecting Ford (Harrison),
She found no comparison,
It was all about St Peter's, Rome.

Monet had style that was fearless,
Cezanne's use of colour was peerless,
But Gaugin was potty,
Seurat was spotty,
And Van Gogh? Well, he was just earless.

Infant Portraits

Jack was red
And Lucy was grey
And Darren was bottle green,

Kelly was blue
And Josh was mauve
And Deb had a yellow sheen.

When the teacher looked up,
She was most upset
That the lesson had come to this,

'But we're only doing
What you said –
To paint each other, Miss.'

The Idea

I had a good idea once,
But my friend poo-pooed it.
Why did he poo-poo my idea?
I've no idea
(Apart from the one he poo-pooed, of course).
What has my idea ever done to him?
Has it ever poo-pooed him?
When he has an idea,
Me and my idea are going to poo-poo it.
He'd better watch out –
There's going to be a lot of poo-pooing about.
And if he ever tries to poo-poo
My ideas again,
He'll find out what poo-pooing
Really means.

Pooem

There it was,
On the pavement,
Right outside the joke shop:
A plastic plop;
A trick turd;
A decoy dump;
A latex log;
A man-made moey;
A joke jobbie;
A bogus botty bomb
Fake faeces;
Sham poo;
Pseudo doo-doo.
How obvious!
So I picked it up.
Oh.

A Quick Word

Mum asked me
If she could have
A quick word
So I gave her
'Velocity'.

She gave me
A piece of
Her mind.

Something Fell on Newton's Head

Something fell
On Newton's Head,
He cried, 'Gravity!'

An apple fell
On Newton's head,
Good job it wasn't the tree.

Listen to This

I've had enough of
your idleness,
your shabbiness,
your noisiness,
your flabbiness,
your cockiness,
your gruffness,
your naughtiness,
your roughness,
your sloppiness,
your badness,
your nastiness,
your madness,
your fussiness,
your grubbiness,
your smugness,
your tubbiness,
your rowdiness,
your artlessness,
your sulkiness,
your heartlessness.
In fact
you're gormless,
you're feckless,
you're gutless,
you're reckless,
you're tactless,
you're careless,
you're brainless
and hairless.

So what have you got to say for yourself?

Sorry.

Time for Arrest

I was arrested
Under the
Law of Averages
Last night.

I suppose
It was
Bound to happen
Sooner or later.

Bullet Points

You know those gangster films
Where the villain says,
'You're history pal...'
And then kills the man?
Well, I think the gangster curriculum
Needs broadening –
How about saying,
'You're geography pal...'
Then kill him in an interesting location?
'You're art pal...'
(Frame him).
'You're maths pal...'
(His days are numbered).
'You're RE pal...'
(A small sacrifice).
'You're English pal...'
(Use bullet points)
'You're French pal...'
(What if he's not?)
'You're PE pal...'
(Run him over).
'You're Information and Communications
Technology pal...'
Maybe not.

The Computer's Excuse for Crashing

You hit my keyboard far too hard,
The scanner's bruised;
My hard drive's scarred.

My monitor has greasy smears,
The printer's been
Reduced to tears.

And the mouse tells me your hands are rough,
He's very shy –
Enough's enough!

Those DVD horrors are starting to freak us,
And just when are you going
To dust the speakers?

My motherboard agrees you're mean,
So here's your reward:
The dreaded blue screen!

Sorry About the Vase, Mum

Sorry mum, the vase got broken.
I was holding it carefully
And the kitchen floor
Came rushing upwards
With tremendous force
And smashed it to pieces.

Actually, mum,
That isn't true at all.

It was the bathroom floor.

Recipe for Disaster

You will need:
A plaice of your own
A pear (although one will do)
As many eggs as you can lay
Your hands on.
Plenty of dough
1 bulb garlic (60 watts max)

Method
1. Take a leek
2. Stop stirring
3. Grate!
4. Beat the eggs and crush the garlic (don't stand for any nonsense)
5. Cool!
6. Cover the bottom of the pan before someone sees it.
7. Buy a sandwich.

Fussy Family

Miy sisster sais I canot spelll.
Shea dusent no wat shea's torking abowt.

My. brother says; i canno't abbreviate"
what? does he! know

My mother says that I sometimes use the wrong words.
Mother, don't be absorb.

My father says that I also get the order of my words muddled.
Huh! Way no.

Spelling Test

The worst thing
To get
In a spelling test
Is diarrhoea.

Proverb

My son, do not belittle.
Bebig.

Big Foot

Big foot,
Massive toes,
Huge eyes,
Tiny nose;

Long ear,
Giant tum,
Wide legs,
Smelly bum.

Busy Afternoon

It was a quiet morning,
Beans for lunch,
Then a busy afternoon:
I...
Tootled my trouser trumpet,
Practised a little bottom barking,
Cut the cheese,
Aired my cheeks,
Played some music downstairs,
Cooked the eggs,
Passed on a message from the interior,
Started the engine,
Stepped on a duck,
Kept the gasman busy,
Dropped a bum note
And then wondered
Where everyone went.

Dodo Doo-doo

Dodo doo-doo?
Itstinct.

The Headmaster's Drone

It has come to my attention
There is litter on the floor.
It has come to my attention
That exam results are poor.

It has come to my attention
That you are incorrectly dressed.
It has come to my attention
That the fire alarm's been pressed.

It has come to my attention
That the lights have been left on.
It has come to my attention
– Oh! Everybody's gone…

About the author

Andy Seed is the sort of person his parents warned him about. He is lofty, nutty, and fairly harmless unless poked with strudel. Andy lives in the wild North but has been known to travel to schools and other places to entertain and rouse with his poetry. To discern more, go to www.andyseed.com.